JUNGLE QUEST

Contents

Jan Burchett
and Sara Vogler

Story illustrated by
Tom Percival

Before Reading

In this story

 Carla

 Rob

 Dad

Introduce these tricky words and help the reader when they come across them later!

Tricky words

- rainforest
- ruined
- Kalonoro
- ghosts
- shiny
- whispered
- gasped
- lemur

Story starter

Carla's and Rob's dad is an archaeologist. He finds out about people who lived long ago. One summer, Carla and Rob went with their dad to the island of Madagascar to help him excavate an ancient ruined village.

The Mystery of the Kalonoro

Carla, Rob, Dad and his team were walking through the rainforest. At last they came to the ruined village.

"If we dig here we should find bits of old pots," said Dad. "They will show us how the people here lived long ago."

Dad's team set up the camp and then they started digging. A man from the nearby village came to see what they were doing.

"You should not dig here," he said. "Bad things will happen."

"What do you mean?" asked Carla.

But just then Carla and Rob heard
one of the team calling.

"Has anyone seen my knife?" he asked.

"I put it on this rock but now it's gone."

"That's funny," said another man, "my
spade has gone too."

"There's something strange going on," said Rob, and he turned to speak to the man from the village. But the man had gone.

That evening Rob and Carla decided to go to the village to speak to the man again.

"It's the Kalonoro!" whispered the man.

"They are taking the tools!"

"Who are the Kalonoro?" asked Rob.

"The Kalonoro are ghosts," said the man.

"They live deep in the rainforest. They
are like wild men. They have long beards
and eyes like fire."

"But why do they want our tools?"
asked Rob.

"Perhaps the Kalonoro don't want you
digging in the ruins," said the man.

Just then an old woman called out,
"If you see a Kalonoro, don't go near it.
They are bad ghosts!"

"I'm afraid of ghosts," said Carla.

"Don't be such a baby," said Rob. "There
are no such things as ghosts. Let's set
a trap and find out who is taking the
tools. We'll leave some tools around
and see who takes them."

Rob went off to get the tools and a torch.

Do you think Carla's trick will work?

Carla was cross that Rob had called her a baby. She decided to play a trick on him. She got some grass and leaves and made a model. She gave the model a long beard and used shiny foil to make two eyes. She hid her model behind a tree and went back to Rob.

Rob had put a pile of tools near the camp.

"Now we'll hide and catch the tool robber," he said.

Carla and Rob hid behind a rock.

Suddenly Carla turned to Rob.

"Did you see that?" she whispered.

"There's something over there," said Carla. "Follow me!" She grabbed the torch and set off towards the tree where she had hidden the model. Rob followed. Suddenly Carla stopped.

"What's that?" she gasped.

"It's a Kalonoro!" yelled Rob. "Run!"
Rob raced back to the camp. Carla
followed him, giggling. Her trick had
worked! Rob was the baby now!

"Dad!" yelled Rob. Dad came out of
his tent.

"What's going on?" he asked.

"We were trying to catch the tool robber,"
said Carla, "and I played a trick on Rob.
He thinks he's seen a Kalonoro but it was
only a model I made."

"You made two models, you mean," said Rob, "and the one in the tree was really spooky. Its eyes flashed like fire!"

"Two models?" gasped Carla. "But I only made one and it wasn't in the tree!"

"Then what *was* in the tree?" whispered Rob. Suddenly there was a noise behind them. Carla and Rob jumped.

"There is your tool robber!" said Dad.
He pointed to an animal that was
running away with the tools. "It's a lemur!
That's what you saw in the tree, Rob."
Carla and Rob looked at each other.
Had Rob seen a lemur in the tree, or was
it a Kalonoro?

Quiz

Text Detective

- Why did Carla make a model of a Kalonoro?
- Do you think it was fair for Carla to play a trick on Rob?

Word Detective

- **Phonic Focus**: Vowel phonemes in polysyllabic words
  Page 9: How many syllables are there in 'afraid'?
  What vowel phoneme can you hear in each syllable?
- Page 7: Find three different speech verbs.
- Page 7: Find a word made of two small words.

Super Speller

Read these words:

through afraid around

Now try to spell them!

Q What do you call a lemur at the North Pole?

A Lost!

Find out about

- The animals and legends of Madagascar

Tricky words

- Madagascar
- lemur
- poisonous
- chameleon
- tongue
- legends
- scary
- lightning

Introduce these tricky words and help the reader when they come across them later!

Text starter

Madagascar is an island covered in rainforest. Strange animals live in the rainforest, such as lemurs, Tomato Frogs, Assassin Spiders and Panther Chameleons. But they are not as strange as the legends about Madagascar.

Myths of Madagascar

Animals of Madagascar

Madagascar is an island off the coast of Africa. A lot of the island is covered in rainforest. Some of the strange animals that live in the rainforest in Madagascar are found nowhere else in the world!

The Lemur

The lemur is found only in Madagascar. There are 50 different kinds of lemur! Some lemurs are as small as a mouse but some are as big as a dog! Lemurs have flowing beards and big bright eyes and some people think they look almost human.

Lemurs live high up in the trees of the rainforest. They eat the fruit that grows up there and they swallow the seeds in the fruit. Then when they do a poo, it falls to the forest floor below and new plants grow from the seeds in the poo.

That is how many new trees grow in the rainforest.

The Tomato Frog

The Tomato Frog is found only in Madagascar. It is the colour of a bright red tomato but this frog isn't good to eat. It has a sticky white spit that stings the skin of any animal. Lots of animals eat frogs but they don't eat the Tomato Frog.

jaws

prey

neck

The Assassin Spider

This spider is found only in Madagascar.

It stabs its prey with its poisonous teeth.

It has a very long neck and it stretches

out its neck to catch insects that fly past.

It looks like a very fierce monster but it

is only 2mm long!

The Panther Chameleon

In Madagascar there are chameleons
that are not found anywhere else in
the world.

People think chameleons change the
colour of their skin to hide, but they really
change colour to show other chameleons
how they are feeling.

A chameleon's tongue is three times as long as the chameleon itself! This means the chameleon does not have to creep up on its food. It catches insects by shooting out its long sticky tongue.

Legends of Madagascar

Some of the animals of Madagascar are very strange but they are not as strange as some of the legends.

The Kalonoro

The legends say that the Kalonoro are strange creatures that live in the forest. The legends say that they have long flowing beards and red eyes that glow in the dark.

The Kalonoro are not very tall but they are very dangerous. If anyone goes near them they will attack them and kill them! Some people think that the Kalonoro with their long flowing beards and big bright eyes are really lemurs.

The Fanany

You would not want to meet a Fanany!
It looks like a snake but it has seven
heads. On each head there is a horn.
The Fanany uses the horn to rip open its
enemies. If anyone comes near a Fanany
it will bite them with its seven mouths.

The Tokantongotra (*say Tok-an-ton-go-tra*)

The Tokantongotra is very scary.

It has two legs that come out of its chest
but it can run like lightning.

It likes to go out at night and eat people!

The Kinoly

The most scary creature is the Kinoly.
It looks like a real person but it has
red eyes and very long finger nails.
If you meet a Kinoly, never ask it why it
has long finger nails. If you do it will say,
"So that I can tear out your liver."
And then it will!

Madagascar is an amazing island. Would you like to go there and see some of the animals that live only in Madagascar? Or would you be too scared? You might meet some of the strange creatures of the legends!

Quiz

Text Detective

- What strange animals live in Madagascar?
- Which legend do you think is the most scary? Why?

Word Detective

- **Phonic Focus**: Vowel phonemes in polysyllabic words

  Page 23: Sound out the four phonemes in 'found'. Is the vowel phoneme long or short?
- Page 24: Why do the words 'Madagascar' and 'People' start with a capital letter?
- Page 25: Why is there an exclamation mark at the end of the first sentence?

Super Speller

Read these words:

animals   attack   scared

Now try to spell them!

Q What do you get if you cross a frog with a fizzy drink?

A Croak-a-Cola.